# MARVEL

## X-MEN

### FIRST CLASS

£7.99

## CHILDREN OF THE ATOM!

The next step in **human evolution** has begun. All over the world, young boys and girls are developing incredible **powers and abilities** that set them apart from the norm. They are Homo Superior - more commonly known as **Mutants.**

## MUTANT MANIA!

Many normal people accept mutants, but there are those who **fear and hate them,** believing this new species to be a threat to humankind. It was for this reason **Professor Xavier** founded the **X-Men.**

## SECRET SCHOOL!

A mutant gifted with **telepathic powers,** Professor Charles Xavier is the headmaster of **Xavier's School For Gifted Youngsters.** But this is one school that holds a big secret. It is in fact a place where young mutants learn how to safely control their powers and also the **X-Men's** base of operation.

# X-MEN?

## X-FORCE!

Professor Xavier knows all too well that there are many **evil mutants** who think Homo Superior should rule over their 'less-evolved' human cousins. It's up to the X-Men to stop these **crazed individuals** and to help make a better world where humans and mutants can live together in **peace.**

## BENEATH THE X-MANSION...

Beneath Xavier's Academy are hidden sub-floors that house the X-Men's holographic training arena the **Danger Room**, the mutant tracking device **Cerebro** and even a hangar for the team's **Blackbird Jet**.

MEET KURT WAGNER, A.K.A. NIGHTCRAWLER--A MEMBER OF THE MUTANT SUPER HERO TEAM THE X-MEN.

GUTEN MORGEN, NEW YORK, I LOVE YOU!

HIS ACROBATIC SKILLS COME FROM GERMANY'S WINDING ROAD CIRCUS. HIS SWASHBUCKLING SPIRIT WAS NURTURED BY A LIFETIME OF ERROL FLYNN MOVIES...

TODAY THEY WILL BOTH BE PUT TO THE TEST.

# REFUGE

SCOTT GRAY story    ROGER CRUZ art    VAL STAPLES coloring    BLAMBOT'S NATE PIEKOS lettering
CRUZ & RUFFINO cover    JOE SABINO production    JORDAN D. WHITE assistant editor    NATHAN COSBY editor
JOE QUESADA editor in chief    DAN BUCKLEY publisher    ALAN FINE executive producer
DEDICATED WITH RESPECT AND ADMIRATION TO LEN WEIN, CHRIS CLAREMONT, JOHN BYRNE AND THE LATE, GREAT DAVE COCKRUM.

JULIE! CHARLOTTE!

MOMMY!!!

HELLLLP!

NO STOP

NO STOP 9AM to 6PM

DON'T WORRY, THEY'RE PERFECTLY S--AAHH!

SWAK

GET YOUR HANDS OFF MY CHILDREN, YOU FREAK!

WHAT IS THAT THING?

IT ATTACKED THOSE GIRLS!

GET IT!

NO STOP 9AM

N-NO! I WAS HELPING!

FILTHY THING!

KRAK

UNNNGH!

I--I WAS HELPING...

WHERE'D IT GO?!

SOME KINDA MONSTER!

DID YOU SEE ITS TAIL?

BAMF

IT WAS A DEMON! IT HAD HORNS, FER PETE'S SAKE!

NOBODY'S SAFE IN THIS TOWN!

ALMOST KILLED THOSE POOR GIRLS...

KLIK

FORTY MILES NORTH OF MANHATTAN, IN WESTCHESTER COUNTY, STANDS XAVIER'S SCHOOL FOR GIFTED YOUNGSTERS.

THE PUBLIC SEES ONLY AN ELITE ACADEMY...

...BUT BEHIND ITS DOORS LIES ANOTHER WORLD.

C'MON, CREW, YOU *KNOW* THIS LEVEL! ARE YOU GONNA LET "G.I. JOEBOT" KICK YOUR MUTATED BEHINDS *AGAIN?*

MY "BEHIND" IS STAYING *UNTOUCHED* TODAY, CYCLOPS!

YEAH, THIS SUCKER'S GOIN' *DOWN!*

HE'S *SHIELDED* AGAINST YOUR LIGHTNING BOLTS, STORM--FIND ANOTHER WAY!

A *MINIATURE BLIZZARD* SHOULD MAKE THE METAL MORE BRITTLE...

CONTINUED ON PAGE 17...

# CEREBRO

| STRENGTH: | 5 |
|---|---|
| INTELLIGENCE: | 5 |
| POWERS: | 7 |
| SPEED: | 4 |
| AGILITY: | 7 |
| FIGHTING SKILL: | 8 |

| STRENGTH: | 4 |
|---|---|
| INTELLIGENCE: | 5 |
| POWERS: | 9 |
| SPEED: | 3 |
| AGILITY: | 5 |
| FIGHTING SKILL: | 7 |

## CYCLOPS ™

An excellent strategist and battlefield technician, Scott Summers leads the X-Men when they are out in the field. A former orphan, he was the very first mutant to be enrolled at Xavier's school and remains the Professor's most loyal pupil.

**Real Name:** Scott Summers
**Powers:** Optical Force Blasts
**Abilities:** Expert pilot, master tactician and a skilled martial artist.

### X-FACT!

Scott's optical blasts fire automatically whenever he opens his eyes. To protect those around him he has to wear either his ruby quartz glasses or his specially constructed visor at all times.

## PHOENIX ™

Jean Grey is an immensely powerful mutant psychic who is able to boost her powers by channeling a mysterious energy known as the Phoenix Force. Though she is currently not an active member of the X-Men, she is always happy to help out on missions if needed.

**Real Name:** Jean Grey
**Powers:** Telekinesis and Telepathy
**Abilities:** Piloting, hand-to-hand combat.

### X-FACT!

When using the Phoenix Force, Jean's telepathy becomes even more powerful than Professor X.

# FILES!

| | |
|---|---|
| STRENGTH: | 5 |
| INTELLIGENCE: | |
| POWERS: | 6 |
| SPEED: | |
| AGILITY: | 6 |
| FIGHTING SKILL: | 9 |

## WOLVERINE™

A master of combat, Wolverine's adamantium claws can cut through just about anything! And it's not just his claws that are enhanced with the super-metal – his bones are too, making him super-tough! Even if he does ever get injured, Wolvie's super-healing factor means he can make a quick recovery in the midst of battle.

*Real Name:* James Howlett
*Powers:* Enhanced senses, healing factor and razor sharp claws.
*Abilities:* Highly skilled martial artist and an expert tracker.

### X-FACT!

Wolverine's past is shrouded in mystery. Even Wolverine himself is unaware of his actual age and orgins!

## SUPER-MUTANT SEARCH

Professor X can locate mutants from all around the world with the telepathy-enhancing abilities of the Cerebro device.

See if you can work out which mutants he's found by matching the mutant to the correct ability...

1) **SUPER-HEALING FACTOR**

2) **ABILITY TO FREEZE ANYTHING**

3) **ABLE TO FLY WITH THE AID OF FEATHERED WINGS**

4) **POSSESSES INCREDIBLE STRENGTH, AGILITY AND INTELLIGENCE IN EQUAL MEASURES**

**BEAST**  **ICEMAN**

**WOLVERINE**  **ANGEL**

# DANGER ZONE!

TURN TO PAGE 62 FOR THE ANSWERS!

The X-Men's rumble in the Danger Room training facility is getting out of control! See if you can spot all 8 changes between these two scenes before the fight's over!

PAH! *NIGHTCRAWLER* COULD SHOW THEM HOW IT IS DONE, YES?

...CONTINUED FROM PAGE 13

HOW WAS THE UNITED NATIONS MEETING, MEDUSA?

TAXING, CHARLES.

I THINK I'D SOONER FACE DOCTOR DOOM THAN ANOTHER GAGGLE OF DIPLOMATS.

BUT WE ARE SLOWLY ACHIEVING OFFICIAL STATUS FOR OUR PEOPLE.

ALLOW ME TO INTRODUCE TWO HOUSE GUESTS--DR. MOIRA MACTAGGERT AND PRINCESS LILANDRA...

IT'S A PLEASURE T' MEET YOU ALL AT LAST!

YOUR NAME IS SPOKEN WITH RESPECT IN THE SHI'AR EMPIRE...

AFTER LUNCH...

SADLY, IT'S AN EVOLUTIONAL IMPERATIVE TO FEAR THE UNFAMILIAR...

YOU ARE A BEAUTIFUL FEMALE FOR A NON-INHUMAN...

YEAH, I TANGLED WITH THE HULK TOO. I LET HIM LIVE...

D'YOU LIKE THAT, BOY? GOOD DOGGIE!

SKRUNCH SKRUNCH

...SO THERE IS A WHOLE CITY OF INHUMANS, TRITON?

IT IS HOME TO MANY THOUSANDS OF MY KIND, KURT WAGNER.

WE ARE AN INFINITELY DIVERSE PEOPLE. NO TWO ARE ALIKE, AND ALL ARE TREATED EQUALLY.

MY CITY'S NAME IS ATTILAN...

...BUT IT IS ALSO KNOWN AS THE GREAT REFUGE.

SO YOU'RE PART OF XAVIER'S *LATEST BROOD*, THEN? I'D HEARD HE'D BEGUN *RECRUITING* AGAIN.

I EXPECT HE'S TOLD YOU OF ME?

Ah...*NO*, HERR FRANK, I DO NOT RECALL HIM MENTIONING YOU...

WE NEED TO FIND YOU A PRESS AGENT, DARLING.

IN MY YOUTH, I SERVED *MAGNETO*. I'M SURE YOU'VE HEARD OF *HIM*.

I CLASHED WITH YOUR TEAMMATES MANY TIMES AS *QUICKSILVER*. AND WHILE I NO LONGER HAVE REASON TO MAKE ANY X-MAN *FEAR* THAT NAME...

...I WOULD SUGGEST YOU DO NOT *GIVE* ME ONE.

Ah, SORRY ABOUT THAT. I'M AFRAID PIETRO'S MUTANT POWER IS *SUPER-SPEED*, NOT *SUPER-CHARM*...

THERE IS NO NEED FOR APOLOGIES, LADY CRYSTALIA.

Oh, JUST CALL ME *CRYSTAL*!

WELL, ARE YOU BOTH READY FOR THE...WHAT IS THE EXPRESSION? THE *"GRAND TOUR"*?

LEAD ON, TRITON...

*LET'S GO SEE ATTILAN!*

ATTILAN IS, AS PROMISED, AN INSPIRING METROPOLIS OF SHINING TOWERS AND NATURAL WONDER.

IT IS A CARNIVAL OF UNIQUE, EXOTIC BEINGS, EACH MORE AMAZING THAN THE LAST.

FOR THE FIRST TIME IN HIS LIFE, KURT WAGNER WALKS FREELY. HIS APPEARANCE ATTRACTS NO STARES, NO REVULSION, NO HORROR.

HE LOVES IT.

CONTINUED ON PAGE 28...

# CEREBRO FILES!

## STORM ™

Storm grew up in Cairo, Egypt but was orphaned from an early age when an aeroplane crashed into her parents' house.

She moved to Kenya to find her ancestral tribe, but also discovered something much more - her mutant powers of control over weather! Treated like a goddess by the tribespeople, she came to the attention of Professor X and joined his X-Men as a key member of the team.

**Real Name:** Ororo Munroe
**Mutant Power:** Full control over elements of weather, including lightning, hurricanes etc.
**Skills:** Hand-to-hand combat

## NIGHTCRAWLER ™

Raised in a travelling circus in Bavaria, Kurt trained as an acrobat, wowing crowds with his exciting skills. But when his mutant powers were discovered by an angry mob, he fled, finding sanctuary with Professor X and his School for Gifted Youngsters in America.

Kurt has also trained in swordsmanship, perfecting the art to an expert level.

**Real Name:** Kurt Wagner
**Mutant Powers:** Enhanced agility, ability to teleport.
**Skills:** Swordsmanship

# THE INHUMANS!

The Inhumans are a secret civilisation who owe their superhuman powers to an alien race known as the **Kree**.

## FROM ANOTHER WORLD...

Thousands of years ago a team of Kree scientists visited Earth to conduct an experiment. They captured a tribe of primitive humans and altered their genetic structures, making them far more intelligent. The Kree's plan was to create a race of superhuman warriors to serve them. The Kree departed, leaving the Inhumans to advance on their own.

## A SECRET CITY

The Inhumans settled on an island in the North Atlantic which they named **Attilan**. They built a magnificent city and developed a technology and culture far beyond any other on Earth. Attilan could be moved, and so they repositioned their city in the Himalayas to avoid discovery. The Inhumans' existence only became publicly known after they encountered the Fantastic Four.

# MIST-IC SCIENCE

An Inhuman scientist called Randac created the Terrigen Mist, a substance which accelerated his people's genetic development. Anyone who bathed in the Terrigen Mist emerged altered, but always with a different mutation and abilities.

## BLACK BOLT ™

The king of the Inhumans
POWERS: His voice is a weapon so loud, he can destroy a mountain with a mere whisper.

## GORGON ™

Blackbolt's cousin, and a mean combatant!
POWERS: Has incredible strength and can create powerful earth tremors with a stamp of his feet.

## TRITON ™

A water-breathing Inhuman with superstrength.
POWERS: Exposure to the Terrigen mist gave Triton supreme skills in water, but he has had to adapt to a life on land.

## KARNAK ™

Another cousin of Black Bolt's, Karnak has never been exposed to the Terrigen mist, but is still impressive in battle.
POWERS: Karnak has trained himself in combat to compensate for his lack of supernatural powers.

## MEDUSA ™

Easily recognised by her impressive hair, Medusa is Black Bolt's Wife and Queen.
POWERS: She can control her long locks to ensnare her opponents and also has super-human speed, strength and endurance.

## LOCKJAW ™

The royal pet, transformed by the Terrigen mist.
POWERS: Has the ability of inter-dimensional teleporting.

...CONTINUED FROM PAGE 24

CONTINUED ON PAGE 38...

# MUTANT SEARCH!

Professor X is monitoring his X-Men and the Inhumans' progress using Cerebro. Can you help him locate all of the Super Heroes in the grid?

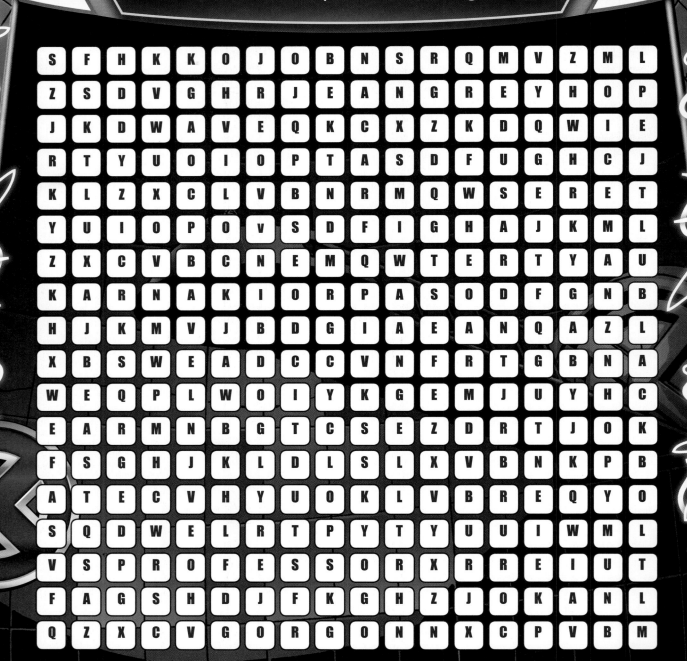

**MEDUSA  BLACK BOLT  GORGON  KARNAK  LOCKJAW  PROFESSOR X**

**ANGEL BEAST CYCLOPS ICEMAN  JEAN GREY  TRITON  WOLVERINE**

# X-Men Art!

## GRAB YOUR PENS...
### WOLVERINE NEEDS YOUR ARTISTIC SKILLS TO BRING HIM TO LIFE!

FIRST, TRACE OVER THE GREY LINES WITH A FINE BLACK PEN TO GIVE HIM SOME PUNCH!

NEXT, USING THE COLOUR GUIDE, USE FELT TIPS OR PENCILS TO BRING SOME COLOUR TO THE SCENE!

## COLOUR GUIDE

# DANGER

The Danger Room is the place where the X-Men practise for missions and make sure their skills are up to scratch. See if you can make it through a training session by solving these puzzles!

### ROBOT RAMPAGE!

**1**

**Warning!** The test arena has been filled with rampaging Kill-Droids. Can you work out how to get to the finish line without running into any of them?

START!

FINISH

### BONUS TEST!

10 X-Men power discs have been hidden throughout the annual. See if you can spot where they all are?

# ROOM!

## IDENTITY CRISIS!

**2** Only one of the Wolverines below is the real thing – the others are holographic copies.
See if your senses are as good as Wolverine's by sniffing out which one matches the original exactly!

**ORIGINAL**

## BLACK OUT!

**3** Prove you're an X-Men X-pert by working out who each of these mutants are just from their shadows!

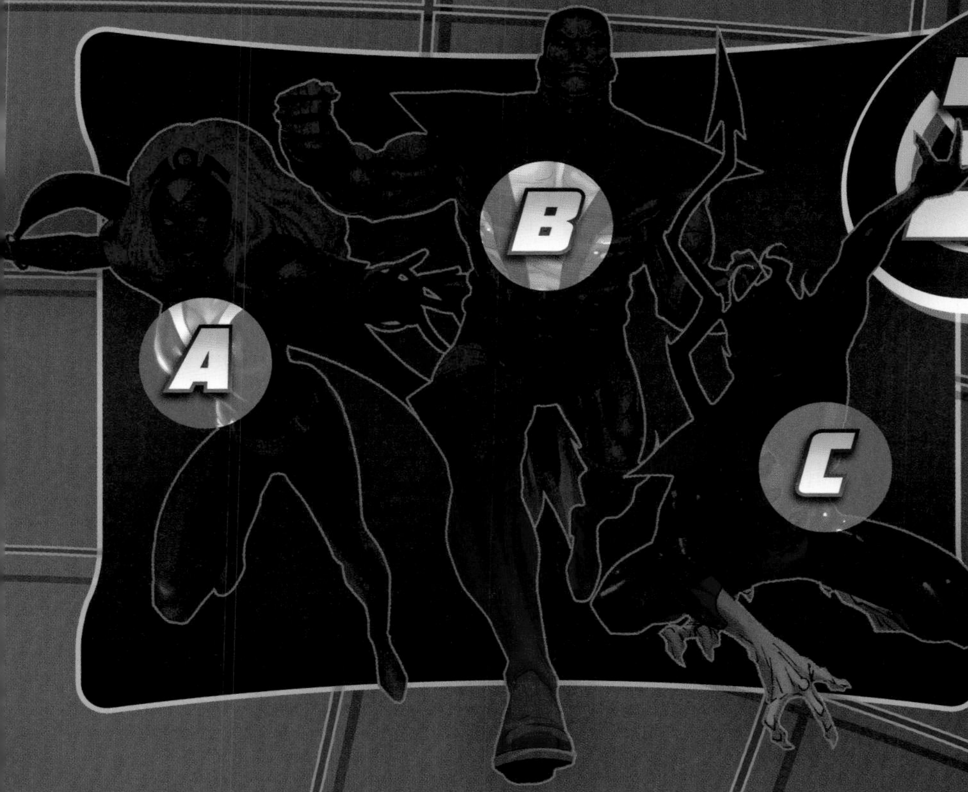

**A**

**B**

**C**

STORM ☐

NIGHT CRAWLER ☐

COLOSSUS ☐

TURN TO PAGE 62 FOR THE ANSWERS!

THE TEMPLE OF RANDAC, IN THE CITY OF ATTILAN...

WHAT HAVE YOU *DONE* TO HIM?!

I STRUCK HIM *DOWN!* HE DESECRATED OUR MOST *SACRED* RITUAL--THE TIME OF *TERRIGENESIS!*

FINISH HIM, OBOROTH!

CRUSH THE DEFILER!

IF YOU HAVE *KILLED* HIM, PRIEST--

HE *LIVES*--THE ENDO-STAFF MERELY PHASES *THROUGH* A BODY, DISRUPTING ITS *BIOFUNCTIONS.*

HE WILL AWAKEN IN *PAIN,* BUT HE DESERVES FAR *WORSE!*

THE ALIEN WILL FACE *JUDGEMENT,* BUT IT IS ONLY A *FORMALITY.* THERE IS BUT *ONE PENALTY* FOR HIS CRIME-- *DEATH!*

NO! IF I MUST FIGHT EVERY INHUMAN IN THIS *CITY,* THEN I SHALL! *YOU WILL NOT HARM HIM!*

PETER RASPUTIN, CALM YOURSELF! MORE VIOLENCE WILL NOT SAVE YOUR FRIEND!

I THOUGHT KURT WAS *YOUR* FRIEND ALSO, TRITON! WAS I *WRONG?*

WE--WE WILL FIND A WAY TO HELP HIM...

NO!

WITH *MY OWN EYES* I SAW THE MUTANT *DEFILE* THE *TERRIGENESIS!*

HOW MANY TIMES HAS ATTILAN BEEN *ATTACKED* BY *OUTWORLDERS?* ENOUGH OF THIS MADNESS! *HE MUST PAY!!!*

BRING **MORE** OUTWORLDERS TO ATTILAN? THAT WOULD ONLY AGGRAVATE THE SITUATION.

WE MUST TRY TO **PLACATE** THE POPULATION...

TRITON, HAVE YOU EVER BEEN TRAPPED IN A WORLD OF STRANGERS-- CUT OFF FROM YOUR LOVED ONES...?

YES... I HAVE.

THEN YOU UNDERSTAND WHAT KURT IS FEELING NOW. LET THE PEOPLE WHO KNOW HIM **BEST** SPEAK ON HIS **BEHALF.**

IT IS HIS **RIGHT.**

VERY WELL.

**FOLLOW ME**-- WE CAN BRING THE X-MEN HERE WITH THE SAME METHOD WE USED TO TRAVEL TO YOUR HOME...

"...LOCKJAW!"

SNOOOAR

NO! TRUST ME, PETER RASPUTIN, THAT WOULD NOT BE **WISE!** DISTURBING LOCKJAW CAN HAVE **SERIOUS** CONSEQUENCES...

FORTUNE **DESERTS** US--LOCKJAW **SLEEPS.** HE SOMETIMES RESTS FOR **SEVERAL** DAYS AFTER A SERIES OF TELEPORTATION JOURNEYS...

THEN I WILL **WAKE** HIM...

SNUGGHH

HE ONCE FOULED **GORGON'S** BEDCHAMBER AND LEFT HIM STRANDED IN **ANTARCTICA.**

WE WILL HAVE TO CONTACT THE X-MEN BY MORE **CONVENTIONAL** MEANS...

SNOARJ

CONTINUED ON PAGE 46...

44

# CEREBRO FILES!

## COLOSSUS ™

By converting the tissue of his entire body into an organic steel-like substance, Colossus gains superhuman strength and a high degree of resistence to bodily harm. He is considered the strongest member of the X-Men, and stands at an impressive 6ft 7in tall!

Born in Russia, he first discovered his powers whilst saving his sister from a runaway tractor. He's not naturally aggressive and prefers to use his great powers to help others in need.

**Real Name:** Piotr Rasputin
**Mutant Power:** Great strength, ability to adopt a metallic form.
**Skills:** Talented artist

## BANSHEE ™

Sean Cassidy is the heir to both a small fortune and a castle in Cassidy Keep, Ireland, where he was born. A reliable member of the X-Men, Banshee has worked as a New York Police Officer and former member of Interpol.

**Real Name:** Sean Cassidy
**Mutant Power:** Sonic 'scream' capable of seriously harming his opponents in battle. He also has the ability of flight.
**Skills:** Hand-to-hand combat, weapons training.

...CONTINUED FROM PAGE 44

DAWN COMES TO ATTILAN. IT IS A SHINING, CLEAR DAY...

...ONE UNPARALLELED IN THE CITY'S HISTORY.

KURT WAGNER, YOU STAND BEFORE THE ROYAL COURT OF ATTILAN...

YOU ARE CHARGED WITH THE WILLFUL DESECRATION OF TERRIGENESIS AND CULTURAL ASSAULT ON THE INHUMAN PEOPLE.

HOW DO YOU PLEAD?

I PLEAD...

I PLEAD FOR A CHANCE TO SPEAK FREELY.

I HAVE KNOWN HATRED IN MY LIFE. I UNDERSTAND WHAT IT IS LIKE TO BE SINGLED OUT, TO BE ABUSED FOR BEING DIFFERENT.

I CAN SEE WHY YOU WOULD WISH TO LIVE HERE, FAR AWAY FROM HUMANITY...

WHEN I CAME TO YOUR CITY, IT SEEMED TO BE MY *DEAREST DREAM* MADE *REAL*--A PLACE WHERE I COULD BE ACCEPTED FOR WHO I TRULY AM.

IT FELT LIKE A WORLD WHERE *APPEARANCE* MEANT *NOTHING.*

BUT THEN I SAW YOUR *RITUAL*, AND I KNEW THAT I WAS *WRONG.*

I AM *APPALLED* BY YOUR BELIEF THAT YOUR CHILDREN REQUIRE "*IMPROVING*"-- THEY ARE *PERFECT* FROM *BIRTH.*

HOW CAN YOU FORCE THEM INTO A *CHAMBER*, MANIPULATE THEIR *GENES*, TRANSFORM THEIR *BODIES?*

HOW CAN YOU MAKE SUCH A DECISION *FOR* THEM, AT SUCH AN *EARLY AGE?* WHAT GIVES YOU THE *RIGHT* TO TAKE THAT CHOICE *AWAY* FROM THEM?

TO SEE PEOPLE AS *GENETICALLY INFERIOR* GOES AGAINST *EVERYTHING* I BELIEVE IN.

THERE WAS *ANOTHER* SOCIETY THAT HELD THE SAME VIEW...

THEY *PLUNGED* THE WORLD INTO THE *DARKEST WAR* IN *HISTORY.*

ENOUGH!

*YOU* ARE THE ONE ON TRIAL HERE, MUTANT!

WE ARE AN *ANCIENT* AND *PROUD* RACE, AND YOU KNOW *NOTHING* OF OUR WAYS! *MY* SPECIES HAD SPLIT THE *ATOM* WHEN *YOURS* WAS STILL CRAWLING IN THE *MUD!*

WHO ARE *YOU* TO JUDGE *US?*

I KNOW YOUR TRADITIONS SPAN *CENTURIES*, BUT A HEALTHY SOCIETY SHOULD ALWAYS HAVE THE CAPACITY FOR *CHANGE*...

I FIND IT TRAGIC THAT, IN A CULTURE WHERE *NO TWO BEINGS* ARE *ALIKE*, YOU SHOULD DEMAND SUCH *CONFORMITY.*

SO....YOU OFFER NO REGRET FOR YOUR ACTIONS?

NONE.

WHAT I *DO* REGRET....IS REJECTING THE WORDS OF A *GOOD FRIEND*--A MAN FAR WISER THAN I.

HE CARED ENOUGH TO MAKE ME FACE A *TRUTH*--THAT I *BELONG* IN THE WORLD, EVEN IF IT *NEVER* WELCOMES ME.

BUT I REFUSED TO LISTEN TO HIM. I *INSULTED* HIM.

I AM *SO SORRY*, PETER.

WHATEVER HAPPENS TO ME, I AM GLAD I HAD THIS CHANCE TO TELL YOU--

WAS IST...?

VRRRRRR

VFOOOOSH

I RECOGNIZE THAT CRAFT-- IT IS *THE X-MEN!*

IMPOSSIBLE! OUR *SENTRIES* WOULD HAVE *ALERTED* US LONG BEFORE THEY REACHED THE *CITY WALLS!*

YEAH, THEY *WOULD*---

UNLESS, OF COURSE, A *TOP-RANK* TELEPATH MANAGED TO *TWEAK* THEIR *PERCEPTIONS* A LITTLE!

BLACK BOLT, *HEAR ME OUT!* WE'RE NOT HERE TO *FIGHT* YOU!

AMEN TO *THAT*---

THIS IS *YOUR* HANDIWORK, TRITON!

PLEASE *LISTEN* TO THEM, MY KING!

LET'S *TALK*, BLACK BOLT--I DOUBT YOU WANT THIS SITUATION ANY MORE THAN WE DO---

NIGHTCRAWLER'S ONE OF *US*. WE'LL FOLLOW YOUR LEAD AS LONG AS IT INSURES HIS *SAFETY*---

NO! SMASH THEM, MY KING!

THE *DEFILER* MUST FACE JUSTICE!

NO MORE OUTWORLDERS!

Hnngh---

JEAN, WHAT'S *WRONG*?

THE CROWD'S *THOUGHTS*, ORORO--L-LIKE A *TIDAL WAVE!* SO MUCH *ANGER*---BOILING--- TEARING--- *SCREAMING*---

C-CAN'T SHUT THEM OUT---

SHUT UP, ALL OF YOU! SHUT UP!

EVERYWHERE WE GO, IT'S THE *SAME*---

*STUPID, UGLY MOBS!*

JEAN---?!

C'MON, KURT, WE'RE GETTING YOU **OUT** OF HERE!

JEAN, **WAIT!** WHAT ARE YOU **DOING?!**

DON'T LET HIM ESCAPE!

THEY HAVE NO RESPECT!

DESTROY THEM!

YOU WOULD TREAT US LIKE **FOOLS,** X-MEN-- LAUGH AT OUR **LAWS,** CONDEMN OUR **CULTURE!** I SAY **NO MORE!**

FOR THE **HONOR** OF **ATTILAN**---

---YOU **WILL FALL!**

YOU FIGHT *WELL*, X-MAN-- BUT I WAS TRAINED FROM INFANCY IN THE MARTIAL ARTS BY THE *PRIESTS* OF THE *WEEPING TOWER*...

*FWOK*

UNNGH!

YOU MAY BE A *SUPERIOR* FIGHTER, KARNAK...

---BUT DID YOUR PRIESTS TEACH YOU HOW TO *TELEPORT*?

*BAMF*

*THWAK*

*SHRKKKK*

THEY DID *NOT.* YOU SEE, I HAVE *NO* ENHANCED POWERS, KURT WAGNER-- ONLY *SKILL.*

I WAS *NEVER SUBJECTED* TO THE *TERRIGEN MISTS.* BUT I AM *STILL* AN *INHUMAN,* AND CONSIDERED IN NO WAY "GENETICALLY INFERIOR"---

...COULD IT BE THAT YOU HAVE JUDGED MY PEOPLE TOO *QUICKLY*?

MY KING, YOU COULD *STOP* THIS BATTLE WITH A *WHISPER!* I *BEG* YOU!

BUT BLACK BOLT MERELY WATCHES...

...AND THE CONFLICT CONTINUES.

CRYSTAL'S ELEMENTAL CONTROL IS AS STRONG AS *MINE*-- AND MY HEAD IS STILL ACHING FROM QUICKSILVER'S PUNCH---

M-MUST CONCENTRATE---

I CAN FEEL YOU *WEAKENING,* STORM!

AN AVALANCHE BEGINS. BOULDERS BLACKEN THE SKY, RAINING DOWN WITH TERRIFYING FINALITY.

OKAY.... JUST SO.... WE'RE ALL CLEAR ON THIS....

I'M.... HOLDING A BILLION TONS OF ROCK BACK.... AND I CAN FEEL.... EVERY OUNCE! I CAN'T....DO THIS.... FOR LONG....

IDEAS.... PLEASE....

TURN YOUR SHIELD INTO A FUNNEL, JEAN!

WE'LL USE IT TO CHANNEL THE ONLY POWER CAPABLE OF DESTROYING THE AVALANCHE....

---BLACK BOLT'S VOICE!

THE INHUMAN MONARCH NODS. A PRIMAL FORCE STIRS WITHIN HIS BODY.

HE RAISES HIS HEAD HIGH...

...AND SPEAKS.

BLACK BOLT HAS BEEN SILENT SINCE INFANCY. NOW THE X-MEN LEARN WHY...

THE AWESOME POWER CONTAINED WITHIN HIS VOICE ERUPTS THROUGH THE FUNNEL, ATOMIZING *EVERYTHING* IN ITS PATH.

A MOUNTAIN VANISHES.

THE HIMALAYAS TREMBLE.

RANDAC BE PRAISED...

ATTILAN *IS SAVED!*

≶Phew≶

THANK GOD...

ME LUNGS ARE FEELIN' A BIT *TEENY* NOW...

BLACK BOLT GIVES THE SIGN OF *TRUCE.* THE BATTLE IS *OVER*...

KURT WAGNER IS *FREE* TO *DEPART.*

AND WHAT OF *THE LAW?*

THE LAW WAS WRITTEN FOR *INHUMANS,* GORGON, NOT *OUTWORLDERS!* THE X-MAN ACTED IN *IGNORANCE* AND WILL BE SHOWN *MERCY!*

AND I WOULD SUGGEST YOU *SHUT* YOUR *GAPING MOUTH*--YOUR *STUPIDITY* TODAY NEARLY BROUGHT ATTILAN'S *DOOM!*

THANK YOU, BLACK BOLT...

WE'VE ALL HAD A TASTE OF THE *NIGHTMARE* THAT COMES WHEN WE STOP LISTENING TO ONE ANOTHER.

OUR PEOPLE HAVE SO MUCH IN COMMON. LET'S NEVER FORGET THAT.

WELL, I DON'T KNOW ABOUT **YOU** GUYS, BUT I'M READY FOR A **LONG SOAK** AND A KING-SIZE TUB OF CHUNKY MONKEY TONIGHT...

CARE TO JOIN ME, FEARLESS LEADER...?

YOUR "FEARLESS LEADER" ISN'T IN THE **MOOD.**

WHAT THE HECK WAS GOING ON IN YOUR **HEAD,** JEAN? THAT FIGHT WAS ENTIRELY DOWN TO **YOU!** IF YOU HADN'T **EXPLODED** LIKE SOME **LUNATIC--**

HEY! I **SAVED THE DAY,** REMEMBER? ATTILAN WOULD BE A **PARKING LOT** WITHOUT ME!

IT WOULDN'T HAVE BEEN THREATENED IN THE **FIRST** PLACE IF YOU HAD JUST **LISTENED** TO ME! YOU HAD NO RIGHT TO BREAK RANKS LIKE THAT!

YOU DIDN'T **FEEL** THEIR **HATRED,** SCOTT! I COULD **SEE** WHAT THEY WANTED TO **DO** TO US!

YOU'RE NOT A **TELEPATH,** YOU DON'T **UNDERSTAND!**

I DON'T UNDERSTAND **YOU** ANYMORE, JEAN.

MAYBE YOU NEVER DID.

YOU GAVE US A NASTY SCARE, KURT...

IT'S GOOD TO HAVE YE BACK SAFE AN' SOUND, LAD!

IF A MAN'S FORTUNE IS MEASURED IN **FRIENDSHIP,** THEN I AM THE WEALTHIEST MUTANT ALIVE. **THANK YOU, ALL** OF YOU...

ESPECIALLY **YOU,** PETER.

YOU ARE VERY WELCOME, TOVARISCH.

BY THE WAY...

WHERE IS **WOLVERINE?**

THE END! 59

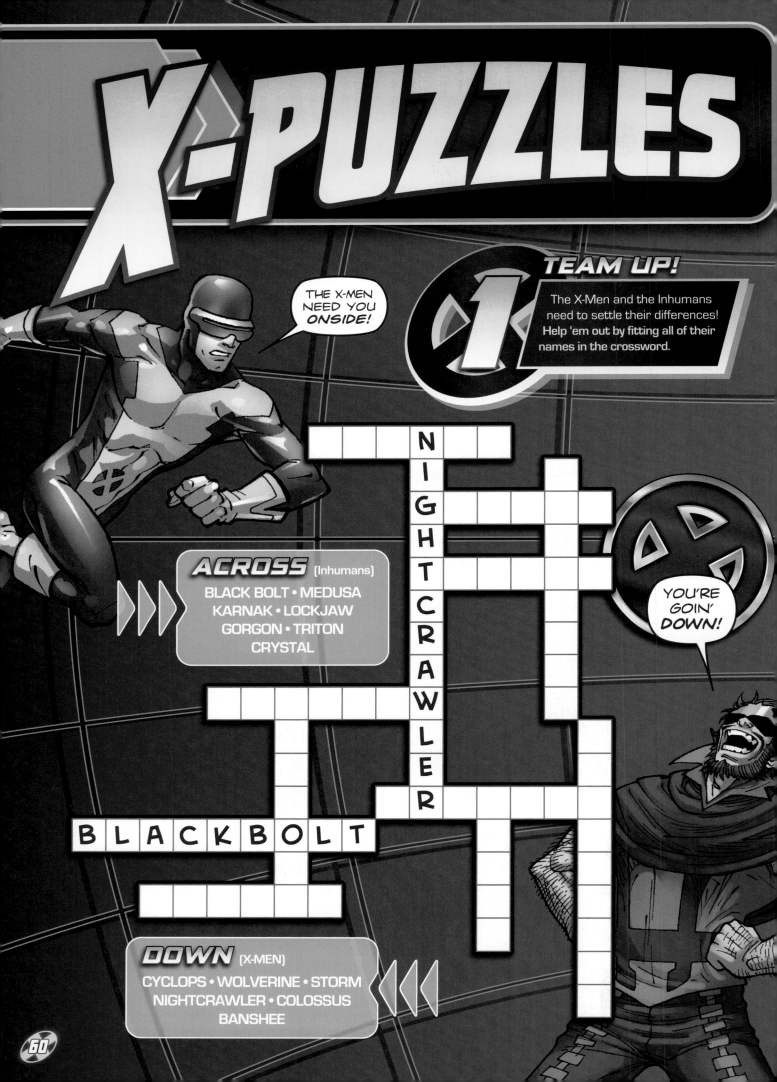

# X-PUZZLES

**THE X-MEN NEED YOU ONSIDE!**

## TEAM UP!

The X-Men and the Inhumans need to settle their differences! Help 'em out by fitting all of their names in the crossword.

**ACROSS** (Inhumans)
BLACK BOLT • MEDUSA
KARNAK • LOCKJAW
GORGON • TRITON
CRYSTAL

**DOWN** (X-MEN)
CYCLOPS • WOLVERINE • STORM
NIGHTCRAWLER • COLOSSUS
BANSHEE

**YOU'RE GOIN' DOWN!**

NIGHTCRAWLER

BLACKBOLT

# THE MISTS OF TERRIGEN!

## 2

The Inhumans' sacred chamber is in tatters! Can you work out which piece doesn't fit?

## 3

### DUAL IDENTITY!

It is customary that the Inhumans should know the true names of the X-Men. Can you help match up their team names to their true identities?

| | | | |
|---|---|---|---|
| **A**  | WOLVERINE | ORORO MUNROE | ☐ |
| **B**  | STORM | SCOTT SUMMERS | ☐ |
| **C**  | CYCLOPS | LOGAN | ☐ |
| **D**  | BANSHEE | PETER RASPUTIN | ☐ |
| **E**  | COLOSSUS | SEAN CASSIDY | ☐ |

TURN TO PAGE 62 FOR THE ANSWERS!

# ANSWERS!

## SUPER-MUTANT SEARCH!

**WOLVERINE**
1) SUPER-HEALING FACTOR

**ICEMAN**
2) ABILITY TO FREEZE ANYTHING

**ANGEL**
3) ABLE TO FLY WITH THE AID OF FEATHERED WINGS

**BEAST**
4) POSSESSES INCREDIBLE STRENGTH, AGILITY AND INTELLIGENCE IN EQUAL MEASURES

**BONUS TEST!**

04, 09, 15, 17, 25, 27, 34, 38, 50, 60

## DANGER ZONE!

## DANGER ROOM!

STORM — A
NIGHT CRAWLER — C B
COLOSSUS — B

## MUTANT SEARCH!

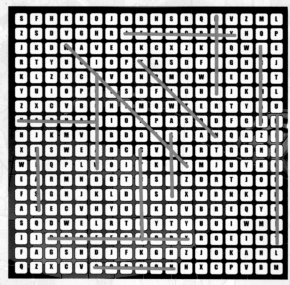

## X-PUZZLES

KARNAK
GORGON
TRITON
COLOSSUS
NIGHTCRAWLER
CYCLOPS
LOCKJAW
CRYSTAL
BLACKBOLT
STORM
WOLVERINE
MEDUSA

| A | WOLVERINE | ORORO MUNROE | B |
| B | STORM | SCOTT SUMMERS | C |
| C | CYCLOPS | LOGAN | A |
| D | BANSHEE | PETER RASPUTIN | E |
| E | COLOSSUS | SEAN CASSIDY | D |